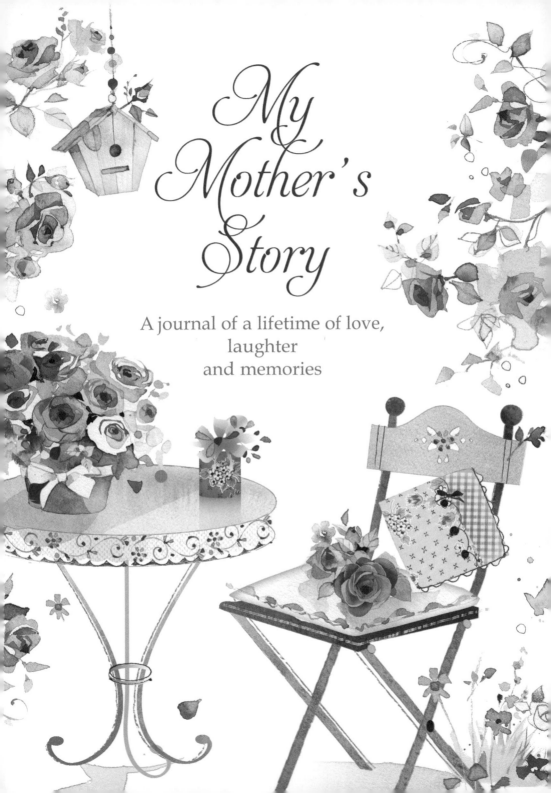

My Mother's Story

A journal of a lifetime of love,
laughter
and memories

First published in 2013. © Like Books & Design Ltd
First published in 2013.
Reprinted 2014, 2015, 2016, 2017, 2018, 2019
Printed in China

This is the story of

_____

completed for

_____

If I could only give you one piece of advice it would be

I was born on

_____

at *[place and time]*

_____

My parents names and ages were

_____

_____

Where we lived when I was born

_____

_____

_____

When I was born, the other members of my family were *[name and age of siblings]*

_____

_____

_____

_____

My grandparents, your great grandparents,
names and ages were

My memories of my grandparents

Fix picture here

Fix picture here

About my mother, your grandmother.
She was born on *[date, place and time]*

_____

_____

She married my father, your grandfather on
[date and place]

_____

_____

About my father, your grandfather.
He was born on *[date, place and time]*

_____

_____

My mother's occupation when I was born

_____

My father's occupation when I
was born

_____

_____

My earliest memories of my parents,
your grandparents

Fix picture here

Fix picture here

My age when I started school was

My first school was

My memories of my first day of school

Memories of my teachers at school

Friends from my first school

Lessons I enjoyed at school

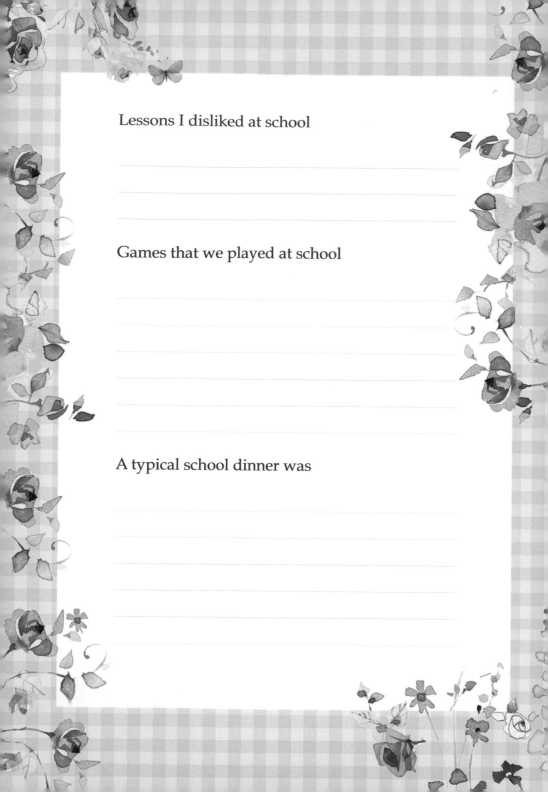

Lessons I disliked at school

Games that we played at school

A typical school dinner was

Fix picture here

The best birthday I had as a child was my

_____

and I remember receiving *[favourite gift]*

_____

_____

_____

The main reason I remember this birthday is

_____

_____

_____

_____

My favourite toy or game was

_____

_____

_____

_____

_____

_____

My favourite books and stories were *[if bedtime stories who read them]*

_____
_____
_____
_____
_____
_____
_____

My favourite nursery rhymes and songs were

_____
_____
_____
_____
_____
_____
_____
_____

The first holiday I remember was *[place]*

in *[month and year]*

We travelled by *[train/car/bus]*

And stayed for *[period of time]*

We went with

Favourite memories of the holiday

The first Christmas I remember was

We spent it *[place and companions]*

My favourite present was

The weather was

Favourite memories of Christmas

My nickname as a child was

The name was given to me by

The reason they chose the name was

The naughtiest thing I did as a child was

Things I most enjoyed doing as a child were
[hobbies/sports/crafts]

My share of the household chores included

My pocket money was

I used to spend my pocket money on
[comics/books/records/treats]

My favourite things to eat and drink were

My least favourite things to eat and
drink were

My bedroom when I was a child [colour scheme, what was in the room, who you shared with]

The best things about my childhood were

Fix picture here

When I was young I wanted to be *[occupation]*

The person I most admired as a child was
[name and reason]

My childhood dreams and ambitions were

I continued with my education until I was *[age]*

at *[place]*

My first job after was
[occupation, age and place]

My first pay-cheque was for
[amount]

This is how my salary was spent *[rent, fashion, hobbies etc]*

My memories of this job are

My favourite top ten records of my teenage
years are *[artist and song title]*

My favourite groups and singers were

My least favourite groups and singers were

The first record that I bought was

The first concert I went to was
[artist, support, venue, date]

Who I went with

My best friends as a teenager were

_____

_____

_____

_____

Our favourite things to do together were

_____

_____

_____

_____

Our favourite places to go were
[coffee shop/night club/movies]

_____

_____

_____

_____

Memories of these friends

The dance "craze" in fashion was

The typical style of make-up was
[heavy eyes/pale lips etc]

The typical hair styles were *[long/cropped/permed etc]*

Words in fashion were
[hip/cool/groovy]

Clothes that were in fashion included

My favourite outfit as a teenager was

My wardrobe was made up of a selection of these clothes

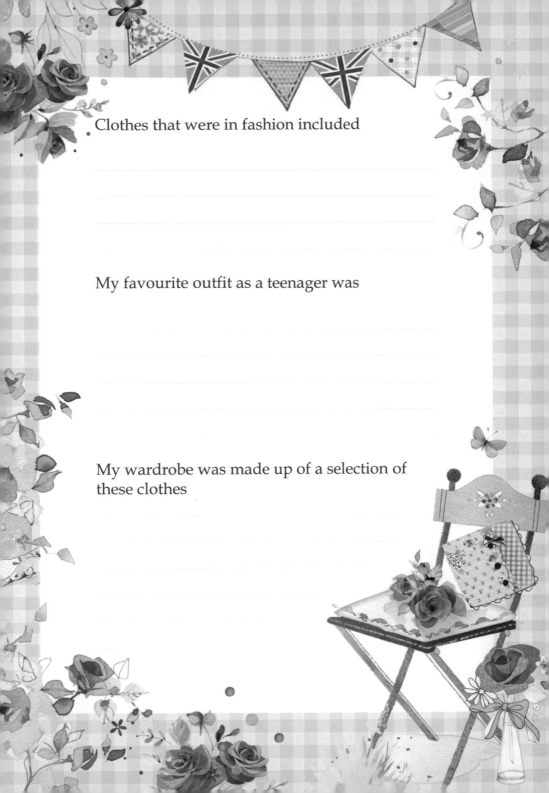

Fix picture here

Fix picture here

My favourite birthday as a teenager was my

and I remember receiving *[favourite gift]*

Where I celebrated and who I celebrated this birthday with

The main reason I remember this birthday is

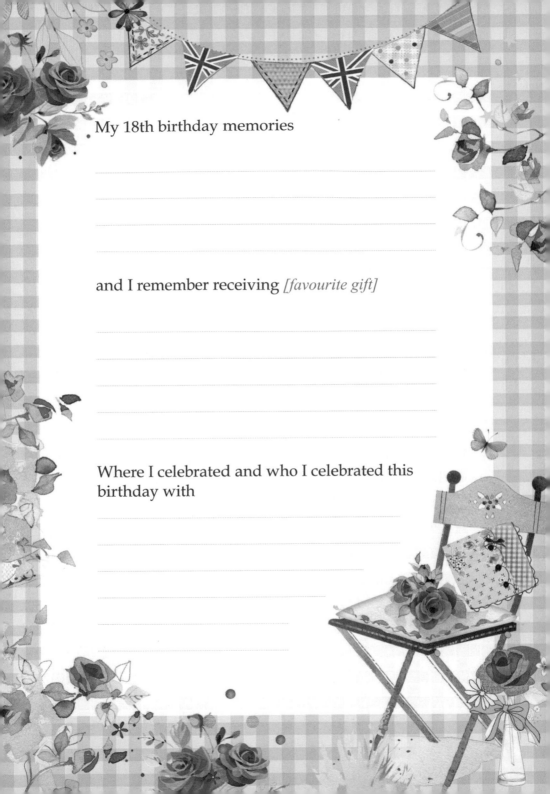

My 18th birthday memories

and I remember receiving *[favourite gift]*

Where I celebrated and who I celebrated this birthday with

Fix picture here

News events on my 18th Birthday

My favourite teenage holiday was *[place]*

in *[month and year]*

We travelled by *[train/car/bus]*

And stayed for *[period of time]*

Who I went with

Favourite memories of the holiday

Fix picture here

Fix picture here

My favourite programmes on TV and Radio were
[name, actor(s), DJ etc]

_____

_____

_____

_____

My favourite movies and actors/actresses were

_____

_____

_____

_____

_____

My favourite books and magazines as a teenager
were *[title and author]*

_____

_____

_____

_____

_____

_____

The hottest summer I can remember was *[year]*

Memories of the hottest summer

The coldest winter I can remember was *[year]*

_____

Memories of the coldest winter

_____

_____

_____

_____

_____

_____

_____

_____

_____

_____

_____

_____

_____

Fix picture here

My favourite Christmas as a teenager was *[year]*

I spent it *[place and companions]*

My favourite present was

The weather was

Favourite memories of that
Christmas

Fix picture here

Fix picture here

My "crush" as a teenager was on

My first boyfriend was called

We met when I was/at

The first date that I went on was *[name and place]*

My first kiss was with
[name and place]

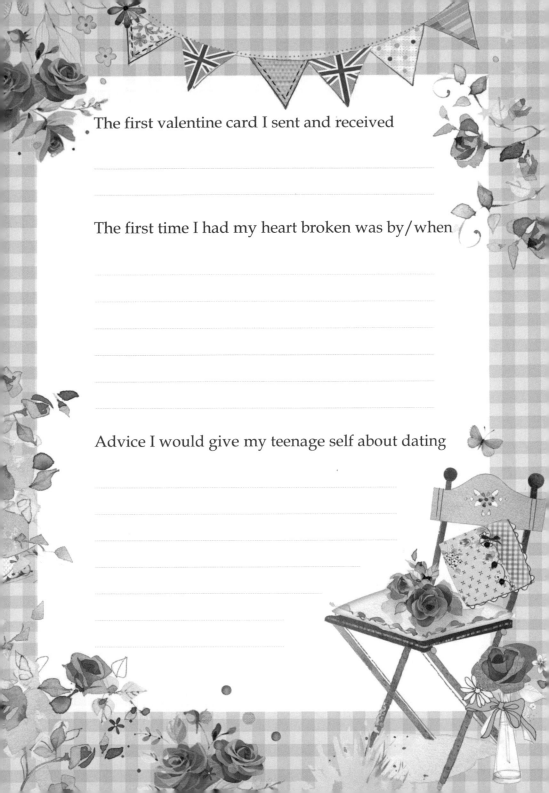

The first valentine card I sent and received

The first time I had my heart broken was by/when

Advice I would give my teenage self about dating

Fix picture here

Fix picture here

The best things about my teenage years were

The worst things about my teenage
years were

When I was a teenager I wanted to be *[occupation]*

The person I most admired as a teenager was
[name and reason]

My teenage dreams and ambitions were

Fix picture here

Your father's full name

_____

He was born on [place and time]

_____

His parents names and ages were

_____

_____

Where he lived when he was born

_____

_____

_____

When he was born, the other
members of his family were
[name and age of siblings]

_____

_____

_____

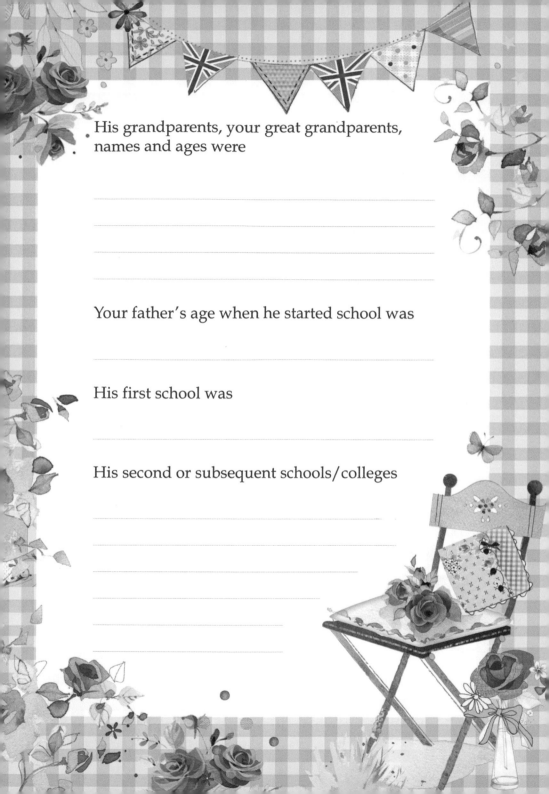

His grandparents, your great grandparents,
names and ages were

Your father's age when he started school was

His first school was

His second or subsequent schools/colleges

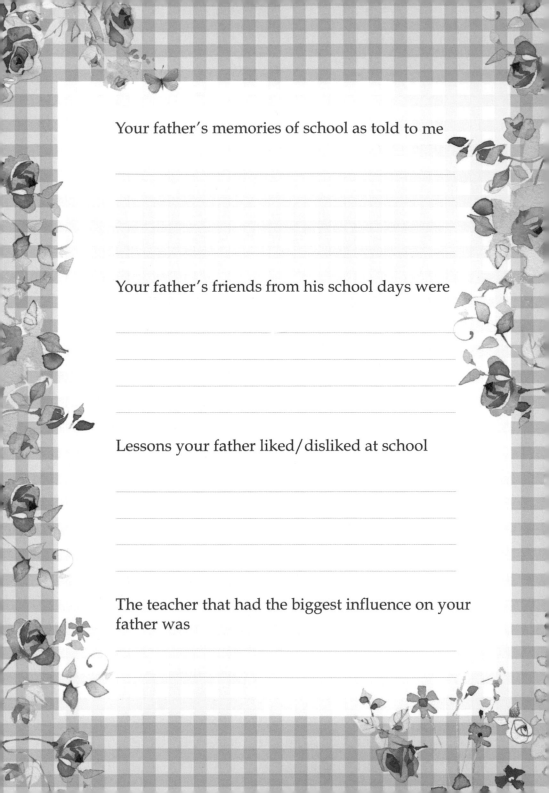

Your father's memories of school as told to me

_____

_____

_____

Your father's friends from his school days were

_____

_____

_____

Lessons your father liked/disliked at school

_____

_____

_____

_____

The teacher that had the biggest influence on your father was

_____

_____

Fix picture here

Your father's nickname as a child was

The name was given to him by

The reason they chose the name was

The naughtiest thing he did as a child was

Things he most enjoyed doing as a child were
[hobbies/sports/crafts]

My first impressions of your father

Fix picture here

Where we first met *[date, place and time]*

_____

What first attracted me to your father

_____

Our first date was *[date, place and time]*

_____

_____

_____

I knew that it was serious when

_____

_____

_____

_____

_____

_____

When I first took your father home to meet my family [date and memories/reactions]

Fix picture here

Fix picture here

Our special song when we were dating was

Our favourite place to go together was

The first movie we saw together was

The first concert we went to together
was *[artist, support, venue, date]*

The first sporting event we went to together was

The first piece of jewellery your father gave me

He gave this to me on *[date and occasion]*

The first time your father bought me flowers was *[date and occasion]*

Fix picture here

Fix picture here

The first holiday I went on with your father was
[place]

_____

in *[month and year]*

_____

We travelled by *[train/car/bus]*

_____

And stayed for *[period of time]*

_____

Favourite memories of the holiday

_____

_____

_____

_____

_____

_____

Fix picture here

Fix picture here

The first Christmas I spent with your father was

We spent it *[place and other companions]*

My favourite Christmas gift from your father

The first gift I bought your father for Christmas

My favourite Christmas memories of your father

Fix picture here

Fix picture here

Our engagement *[date, place and about the proposal]*

Our engagement party

We married on *[date, time and place]*

My bridesmaids were

Your father's best man and ushers were

The reception was held at

Fix picture here

Fix picture here

The flowers in my bouquet were

My wedding dress was

Our first dance together was

We choose it because

Special memories of the day

Fix picture here

Fix picture here

My first thoughts when I found out that I was expecting you

_____

_____

_____

_____

_____

_____

During my pregnancy with you
[cravings/morning sickness/feelings]

_____

_____

_____

_____

_____

_____

The labour itself was

My thoughts on seeing you for the first time

Fix picture here

Fix picture here

You were born on *[date, place and time]*

Present at your birth

Your weight was

You looked like

Your first visitors were

How we chose your name, its meaning and
names you nearly had

Fix picture here

Fix picture here

We took you home on

The weather was

Your first night at home we

Your favourite soft toy was

The colours and theme of your nursery

Your favourite nursery rhymes and lullabies

Your favourite bedtime stories

Your favourite meals

Stuff you really didn't like

You slept through the night when you were

You got your first tooth when you were

You started to crawl at

You started to walk at

Bathtime was *[happy/scary/noisy]*

The first words that you said were

My favourite outfit on you when you were a baby was

_____

_____

_____

Your first holiday as a baby was to *[place]*

_____

You were *[age]*

_____

We travelled by *[train/car/bus]*

_____

And stayed for *[period of time]*

_____

Favourite memories of the holiday

_____

_____

Fix picture here

Fix picture here

Your first Christmas was celebrated with

at

Your first Christmas gifts were

Favourite memories of that Christmas

Fix picture here

Fix picture here

Your nickname as a baby was

The name was given to you by

The reason behind the name was

Things you loved to do/hated to do

My dreams and ambitions for you as a baby

Fix picture here

Fix picture here

The first year we had a birthday party for you was *[age]*

_____

at *[place and time]*

_____

_____

Guests included

_____

_____

_____

_____

Memories of the party include

_____

_____

_____

_____

_____

_____

Your first day of school I

Your first part in a school play was

You learnt to ride a bike when you were

You learnt to swim when you were

Your favourite books and magazines were

Your favourite TV programmes were

Your favourite groups and singers were

Fix picture here

Your favourite colour to wear

Your favourite pair of shoes

Your favourite outfit

The first time you dressed in fancy-dress you were *[age and occasion]*

Games you loved playing were

Things that made you laugh as a child

Funny things you used to say

The funniest thing you did when you were young

The most embarrassing thing you did when you were young

Fix picture here

Fix picture here

Things that I wish I had done differently when you were a child

_____

_____

_____

_____

The best things I remember about your childhood were

_____

_____

_____

_____

_____

_____

_____

As you grow, the things about you that make me most proud are

Fix picture here

Fix picture here

January

Complete with special dates to remember

1st	
2nd	
3rd	
4th	
5th	
6th	
7th	
8th	
9th	
10th	
11th	
12th	
13th	
14th	
15th	

16th

17th

18th

19th

20th

21st

22nd

23rd

24th

25th

26th

27th

28th

29th

30th

31st

January

February

1st	
2nd	
3rd	
4th	
5th	
6th	
7th	
8th	
9th	
10th	
11th	
12th	
13th	
14th	
15th	

16th

17th

18th

19th

20th

21st

22nd

23rd

24th

25th

26th

27th

28th

29th

February

March

1st	
2nd	
3rd	
4th	
5th	
6th	
7th	
8th	
9th	
10th	
11th	
12th	
13th	
14th	
15th	

16th

17th

18th

19th

20th

21st

22nd

23rd

24th

25th

26th

27th

28th

29th

30th

31st

March

April

1st	
2nd	
3rd	
4th	
5th	
6th	
7th	
8th	
9th	
10th	
11th	
12th	
13th	
14th	
15th	

| 16th |
| 17th |
| 18th |
| 19th |
| 20th |
| 21st |
| 22nd |
| 23rd |
| 24th |
| 25th |
| 26th |
| 27th |
| 28th |
| 29th |
| 30th |

April

May

1st	
2nd	
3rd	
4th	
5th	
6th	
7th	
8th	
9th	
10th	
11th	
12th	
13th	
14th	
15th	

16th

17th

18th

19th

20th

21st

22nd

23rd

24th

25th

26th

27th

28th

29th

30th

31st

May

June

Complete the calendar with dates to remember

1st	
2nd	
3rd	
4th	
5th	
6th	
7th	
8th	
9th	
10th	
11th	
12th	
13th	
14th	
15th	

| 16th |
| 17th |
| 18th |
| 19th |
| 20th |
| 21st |
| 22nd |
| 23rd |
| 24th |
| 25th |
| 26th |
| 27th |
| 28th |
| 29th |
| 30th |

June

July

1st	
2nd	
3rd	
4th	
5th	
6th	
7th	
8th	
9th	
10th	
11th	
12th	
13th	
14th	
15th	

16th

17th

18th

19th

20th

21st

22nd

23rd

24th

25th

26th

27th

28th

29th

30th

31st

July

August

1st	
2nd	
3rd	
4th	
5th	
6th	
7th	
8th	
9th	
10th	
11th	
12th	
13th	
14th	
15th	

16th
17th
18th
19th
20th
21st
22nd
23rd
24th
25th
26th
27th
28th
29th
30th
31st

August

September

1st	
2nd	
3rd	
4th	
5th	
6th	
7th	
8th	
9th	
10th	
11th	
12th	
13th	
14th	
15th	

16th

17th

18th

19th

20th

21st

22nd

23rd

24th

25th

26th

27th

28th

29th

30th

September

October

1st	
2nd	
3rd	
4th	
5th	
6th	
7th	
8th	
9th	
10th	
11th	
12th	
13th	
14th	
15th	

16th

17th

18th

19th

20th

21st

22nd

23rd

24th

25th

26th

27th

28th

29th

30th

31st

October

November

1st	
2nd	
3rd	
4th	
5th	
6th	
7th	
8th	
9th	
10th	
11th	
12th	
13th	
14th	
15th	

16th
17th
18th
19th
20th
21st
22nd
23rd
24th
25th
26th
27th
28th
29th
30th

November

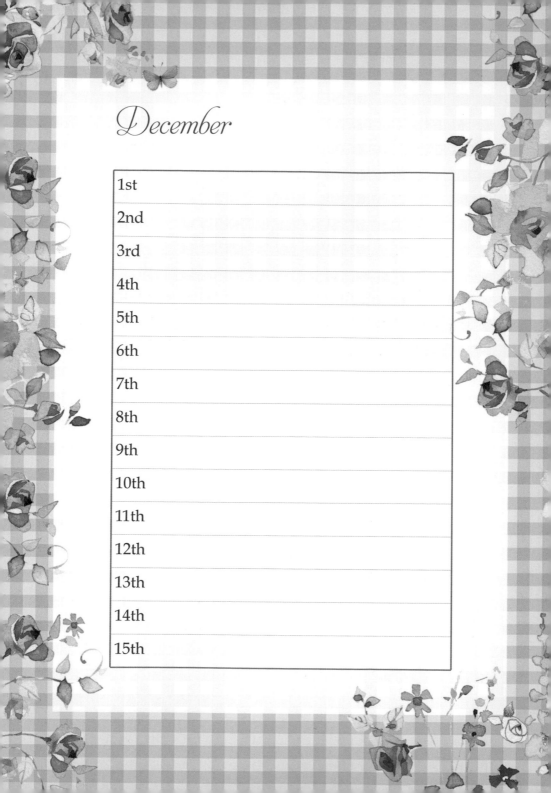

December

1st	
2nd	
3rd	
4th	
5th	
6th	
7th	
8th	
9th	
10th	
11th	
12th	
13th	
14th	
15th	

16th	
17th	
18th	
19th	
20th	
21st	
22nd	
23rd	
24th	
25th	
26th	
27th	
28th	
29th	
30th	
31st	

December

The happiest and greatest moments of my life
have been